*This book is dedicated to*

MAGGIE

THIS FIRST EDITION OF
NURSERY SONGS AND
RHYMES PICTURED
IN BLACK AND WHITE BY
WINIFRED SMITH,
IS PRINTED ON DUTCH HAND-
MADE PAPER, IN A LIMITED
ISSUE OF 1000 COPIES ONLY;
FUTURE EDITIONS WILL BE PULL-
ED ON AN ANTIQUE PAPER.

# NURSERY · SONGS · & · RHYMES
## OF ENGLAND
### PICTURED · IN · BLACK · & · WHITE
— BY —
## WINIFRED · SMITH

BO-PEEP

BOY BLUE

1895

PUBLISHED · BY · DAVID · NUTT · IN · THE · STRAND

© 1993 PRYOR PUBLICATIONS

75 Dargate Road, Yorkletts, Whitstable
Kent CT5 3AE

Tel. & Fax: (0227) 274655

ISBN 0946014 14 0
A CIP RECORD FOR THIS BOOK IS AVAILABLE
FROM THE BRITISH LIBRARY.

Printed and bound by
Whitstable Litho Printers Ltd., Whitstable

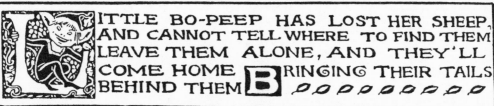

ITTLE BO-PEEP HAS LOST HER SHEEP,
AND CANNOT TELL WHERE TO FIND THEM
LEAVE THEM ALONE, AND THEY'LL
COME HOME BRINGING THEIR TAILS
BEHIND THEM

Little Bo-peep has lost her sheep,
And cannot tell where to find them;
Leave them alone, and they'll come home,
And bring their tails behind them.

Little Bo-peep fell fast asleep,
And dreamt she heard them bleating
But when she awoke she found it a joke,
For still they all were fleeting.

Then up she took her little crook,
Determined for to find them;
She found them indeed, but it made her heart bleed,
For they'd left their tails behind them.

# SING A SONG OF SIXPENCE

Sing a song of sixpence, a pocket full of rye,
Four and twenty blackbirds baked in a pie;
When the pie was opened the birds began to sing
Was not that a dainty dish to set before the king.

The king was in his counting house, counting
O O O O out his money; O O O O
The queen was in the arbour, eating bread
and honey;
The maid was in the garden hanging out
the clothes,
There came a little blackbird and snapt
off her nose.

# SING·A·SONG·OF·SIXPENCE

The maid was in the garden hanging out the clothes, | There came a little blackbird and snapt off her nose.

# RIDE - A - COCK - HORSE

Ride a cock-horse to Banbury Cross,
To see a fine lady get on a white horse;
With rings on her fingers and bells on her toes,
She shall have music wherever she goes.

# DING · DONG · BELL

Ding, dong, bell; Pussy's in the well.
Who put her in? Little Tommy Lin.
Who pulled her out? Little Tommy Stout.
What a naughty boy was that
To drown poor Pussy Cat.

Curly locks! curly locks! wilt thou be mine?
Thou shalt not wash dishes, nor yet feed the swine
But sit on a cushion and sew a fine seam,
And feed upon strawberries sugar and cream.

# PAT-A-CAKE. PAT-A-CAKE

Pat-a-cake, pat-a-cake, baker's man,
Bake me a cake as fast as you can;
Pat it and prick it and mark it with T,
And put it in the oven for Tommy and me.

# LITTLE · JACK · HORNER

Little Jack Horner sat in the corner,
    Eating his Christmas pie; ⌐plum,
He put in his thumb, and pulled out a
    And said "What a good boy am I!"

# HUMPTY DUMPTY

Humpty Dumpty sat on a wall,
Humpty Dumpty had a great fall,
"All the king's horses and all the king's men
Could not set Humpty Dumpty up again."

Pussy-cat, Pussy-cat, where have you been?
I've been to London to look at the Queen.
Pussy-cat, Pussy-cat, what did you there?
I frightened a little mouse under her chair.

# THERE WAS AN OLD WOMAN

There was an old woman who lived
in a shoe,
She had so many children she didn't
know what to do;
She gave them some broth without
any bread,
She whipped them all well and put
them to bed.

GOOD KING ARTHUR

# GOOD KING ARTHUR

When good King Arthur ruled this land,
    He was a goodly king;
He stole three pecks of barley – meal,
    To make a bag-pudding.

A bag-pudding the queen did make,
    And stuffed it well with plums :
And in it put great lumps of fat,
    As big as my two thumbs.

The king and queen did eat thereof,
    And noblemen beside ;
And what they could not eat that night,
    The queen next morning fried.

THERE·WAS·AN·OLD·WOMAN·AS·I'VE·HEARD·TELL

There was an old woman, as I've heard tell,
She went to market her eggs for to sell;
She went to market all on a market day,
And she fell asleep on the king's highway.

There came by a pedlar, whose name was Stout,
    He cut her petticoats all round about;
    He cut her petticoats up to the knees,
Which made the old woman to shiver and freeze.

When the little old woman first did wake,
She began to shiver, and she began to shake;
She began to wonder, and she began to cry,
"Lauk a daisy on me, this can't be I!"

    "But if it be I, as I hope it be,
I have a little dog at home, and he'll know me;
    If it be I, he will wag his little tail,
And if it be not I, he will loudly bark and wail."

Home went the little woman all in the dark,
Up got the little dog and he began to bark;
He began to bark,    so she began to cry,
"Lauk a daisy on me, this is none of I!"

# ✳ ✳ ✳ I HAVE A LITTLE SISTER ✳ ✳ ✳

I have a little sister, they call her Peep, Peep;
She wades the water, deep, deep, deep;
She climbs the mountains, high, high, high.
Poor little thing! she has but one eye.

# SIMPLE SIMON

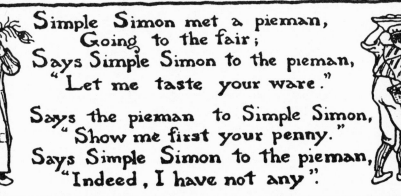

Simple Simon met a pieman,
Going to the fair;
Says Simple Simon to the pieman,
"Let me taste your ware."

Says the pieman to Simple Simon,
"Show me first your penny."
Says Simple Simon to the pieman,
"Indeed, I have not any".

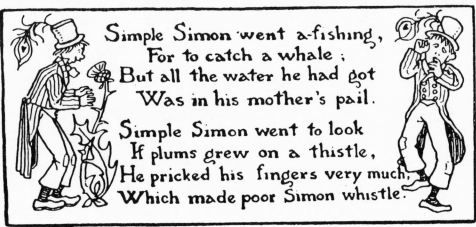

Simple Simon went a-fishing,
    For to catch a whale ;
But all the water he had got
    Was in his mother's pail.

Simple Simon went to look
    If plums grew on a thistle,
He pricked his fingers very much,
    Which made poor Simon whistle.

# OLD · KING · COLE

Old King Cole , was a merry old soul,
And a merry old soul was he ;
He called for his pipe, and he called for his bowl,
And he called for his fiddlers three .
Every fiddler he had a fiddle
And a very fine fiddle had he ;          fiddlers
Twee tweedle dee, tweedle dee went the
Oh! theres none so rare, as can compare
With King Cole and his fiddler's three.

A pretty little girl in a round-eared cap
Met me in the streets t'other day; [went bump;
She gave me such a thump, that my heart it
I thought I should have fainted away!
I thought I should have fainted away!

# CROSS PATCH

Cross patch, draw the latch,
Sit by the fire and spin;
Take a cup and drink it up,
Then call your neighbours in.

# BARBER SHAVE A PIG

Barber, barber, shave a pig,
How many hairs will make a wig;
"Four-and-twenty, that's enough,"
Give the barber a pinch of snuff.

# HARK! HARK! THE DOGS DO BARK·

Hark! hark! the dogs do bark,
Beggars are coming to town;
Some in jags, some in rags,
And some in velvet gowns.

# BOY BLUE

Little Boy Blue, come blow up your horn,
The sheep's in the meadow, the cow's in the corn
Where's the little boy that looks after the sheep?
He is under the hay-cock fast asleep.
Will you wake him? No not I ;
For if I do, he'll be sure to cry.

# THE QUEEN OF HEARTS

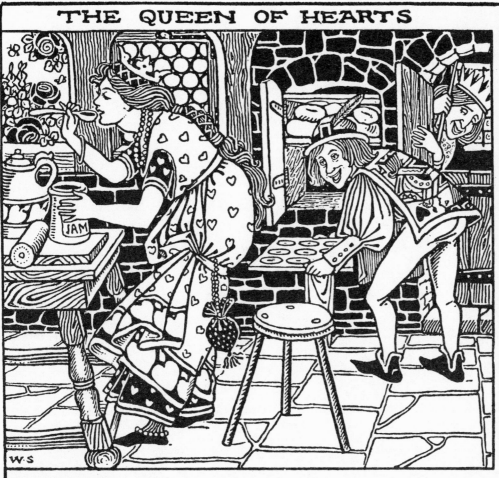

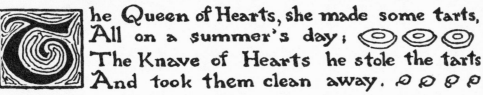

The Queen of Hearts, she made some tarts,
All on a summer's day;
The Knave of Hearts he stole the tarts
And took them clean away.

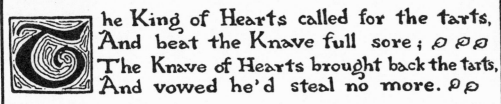

The King of Hearts called for the tarts,
And beat the Knave full sore;
The Knave of Hearts brought back the tarts,
And vowed he'd steal no more.

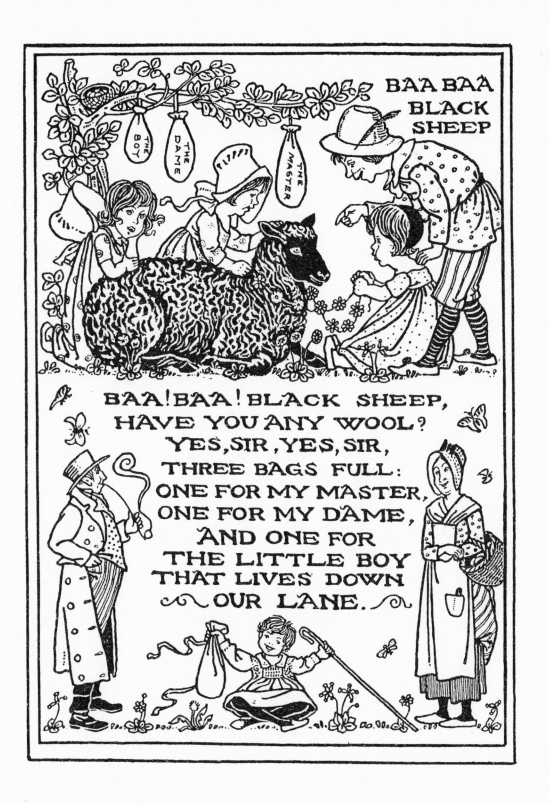

BAA BAA
BLACK
SHEEP

BAA! BAA! BLACK SHEEP,
HAVE YOU ANY WOOL?
YES, SIR, YES, SIR,
THREE BAGS FULL:
ONE FOR MY MASTER,
ONE FOR MY DAME,
AND ONE FOR
THE LITTLE BOY
THAT LIVES DOWN
OUR LANE.

# MISTRESS MARY

Mistress Mary, quite contrary,
How does your garden grow?
Silver bells, and cockle shells,
And pretty maids all in a row.

Mistress Mary, quite contrary,
How does your garden grow?
Silver bells and cockel shells,
And pretty maids all in a row.

# LITTLE MISS MOPSEY

Little Miss Mopsey,
She sat in the shopsey
Eating of curds and whey;
There came a great spider,
And sat him down beside her,
And frightened Miss Mopsey away.

# LITTLE TOM TUCKER

Little Tom Tucker sings for his supper;
What shall he eat? white bread and butter.
How shall he cut it without e'er a knife?
How will he marry without e'er a wife?

WINIFRED SMITH did much of her illustrative work in the 1890's; attended Birmingham School of Art, and was influenced by the Gaskins and other members of the Birmingham circle. She illustrated the two series of *Children's Singing Games*, the text being by Alice Gomme. In 1894 *The Bookman* described her as being an artist 'whose designs in black and white are witty, pretty and effective.'

In 1895, *Nursery Songs and Rhymes of England Pictured in Black and White* was published, probably her greatest achievement as an artist. In 1896 she won commendation in the National Competition at South Kensington, and *The Studio* magazine illustrated her work.

PETER STOCKHAM
*(February 1993)*

# OTHER BOOKS AVAILABLE
# FROM PRYOR PUBLICATIONS

## Don't: A Manual of Mistakes and Improprieties more or less prevalent in Conduct and Speech. By CENSOR.

*UNMUTILATED and with the additional matter. The only Authorised and COMPLETE Edition.* £3.50

## English As She Is Spoke: OR A JEST IN SOBER EARNEST.

*"Excruciatingly funny"*—THE WORLD. £3.50

## CHRISTMAS ENTERTAINMENTS

Illustrated with many diverting cuts—a reprint of the very amusing and scarce 1740 edition, an original copy of which would now command more than twice its weight in gold. £3.50

## Why Not Eat Insects? "Them insecs eats up every blessed green thing that do grow, and us farmers starves."

"Well, eat *them*, and grow fat!" £3.50

## A PLAIN COOKERY BOOK FOR THE WORKING CLASSES

*from an original copy published in 1861.*

## BY CHARLES ELMÉ FRANCATELLI
### LATE MAÎTRE D'HÔTEL AND CHIEF COOK TO HER GRACIOUS MAJESTY QUEEN VICTORIA

It contains recipes such as "Baked Bullocks Hearts," "Treacle Pudding," "Giblet Pie," "Sheep Pluck," "Cow Meal Broth" and "Rice Gruel, a Remedy for Relaxed Bowles." £3.75

CHILDREN'S SINGING GAMES

1894

This facsimile of Children's Singing Games, first published in 1894, will also appeal very much to adults in their own right.

There are eight games with words, music and instructions on playing, together with an explanation of their origins. Most striking are the superb Line illustrations.

This enchanting book gives a refreshing glimpse of part of our heritage almost forgotten about in this age of alternative children's entertainments.

A second series will be publishes in due course.

*Price* **£7.**⁹⁹

---

"Buy a fine Singing Bird?"

# Old London Cries

A quality reprint of an 1885 edition with over 140 pages of informative and interesting reading, together with over 50 woodcuts depicting various street traders of London from the seventeenth century.

*Price*
**£6.**⁹⁵

*ALL POST FREE*
A full list of our publications sent free on request.

### PRYOR PUBLICATIONS
75 Dargate Road, Yorkletts, Whitstable , Kent CT5 3AE
Tel. & Fax: (0227) 274655